The Lazy
Young Duke
of
Dundee

by William Wise

pictures by Barbara Cooney

RAND McNALLY & COMPANY
Chicago   New York   San Francisco

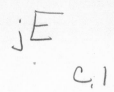

To my brother ROBERT

IN DAYS LONG AGO,
When most people, you know,
Kept as busy as busy could be,

In a castle of stone
Lived a knight who was known
As the Lazy Young Duke of Dundee.

"It's so pleasant," he said,
"To lie curled up in bed
  For hours and hours past dawn,

"Which I do until ten,
  Take a shower, and then
  Eat my bacon and eggs on the lawn.

"All the rest of the day
  I nap, or I play
  On the lute, or the flute, or guitar,

"While at night, through my 'glass,'
  I watch meteors pass,
  And keep charts of moon, planet, and star.

"And I have to confess
  That I'm lucky, I guess,
  For no worries or woes trouble *me*.

"So who cares if I'm known
  In my castle of stone
  As the Lazy Young Duke of Dundee?"

Now one morning, by chance,
All his uncles and aunts
Came to visit him over the glen.

But when they drew near
His loud snores they could hear,
And they knew he was sleeping again.

Cried his uncles—three Earls—
"By-the-bagpipe-that-skirls!
Our young kinsman is not on the ball!"

While his aunts—ladies prim—
Said, "The trouble with *him*
Is the loafer does no work at all!"

So they took him aside
Out of strong family pride
And they gave him these words of advice:

"A young laird in his prime
Shouldn't sleep all the time,
As we've mentioned before, once or twice!

"*Other* young knights we know
Have some get-up-and-go;
They don't languish about on divans.

"They keep busy with plots,
  Ambuscades, and sneak shots,
  And with bold and nefarious plans.

"Take Sir Angus MacClane,
  Our great trial and bane,
  For our clan he detests and deplores.

"He'll ride off day or night
  Just to find a good fight.
  He's a fellow who's been to the wars!

"Now the upshot is clear,
  People hold him in fear,
  So his castle is safe from all foes.

"And yours would be too,
  If only you'd do
  The intelligent things we propose.

"But the future is plain
  If you choose to remain
  Just as idle as idle can be.

"Yes, it's DOOM, once you're known
  In your castle of stone
  As the Lazy Young Duke of Dundee!"

Well, they hardly had spoken
When the silence was broken
By a hideous howl from the glen.

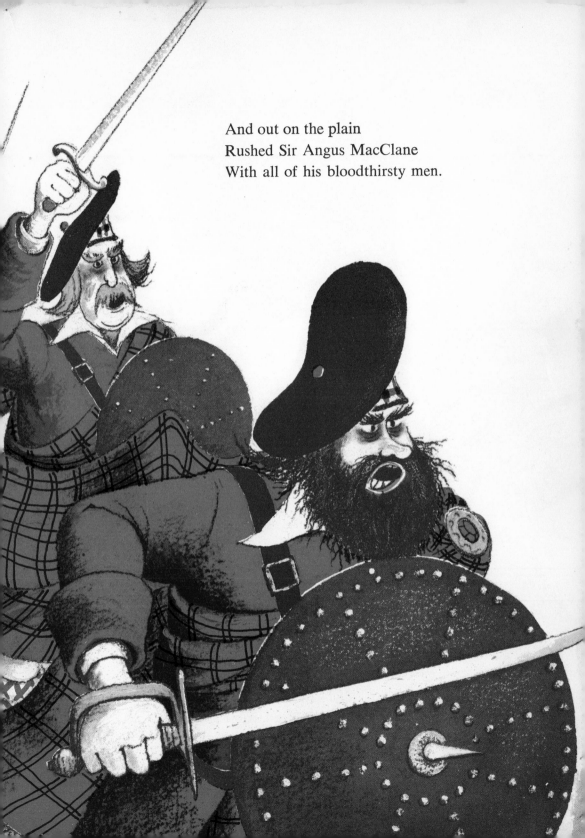

And out on the plain
Rushed Sir Angus MacClane
With all of his bloodthirsty men.

"It's a trap!" cried the Earls,
"By-the-bagpipe-that-skirls!
  He has hatched a most sinister plot!"

Cried the aunts, "Gloom and Woe!
We are caught by the foe!
  Our whole clan's in a terrible spot!

"See, MacClane's everywhere,
Dashing here, dashing there,
He'll surround us in six seconds flat!

"We have nowhere to run.
We're completely undone.
We'll surrender—and that will be that!"

Said one Earl, "Not so quick!
He has played us a trick,
But there's no need to yield to such fears,

"As it's very well known
In a castle of stone
You can hold out for hundreds of years.

"So why babble or brood?
We'll have plenty of food,
And we'll live here in comfort and ease,

"Till Sir Angus MacClane
Finds the siege is in vain
And begs us for peace on his knees!"

Then the Duke of Dundee
Said, "I'd like to agree,
Since in all things I wish to obey you,

"But I think you should know
That my food stocks are low—
I do hope that the news won't dismay you.

"For some weeks now, I guess
It's a month more or less,
I've been *meaning* to go to the store . . .

"But with charting the Moon,
And with keeping in tune
My new lute, which is truly a chore . . .

"Well, the facts I won't hide,
I just let the thing slide,
And of victuals there's little to share.

"All the food that I've got
Wouldn't fill a small pot.
The sad truth is—my cupboard is bare!"

"AH!" they screamed all at once,
"You infernal young dunce!"
    (And one Earl *might* have muttered a curse)

" 'Don't be lazy!' we've said,
  'If you lounge in your bed
    It will lead to disaster—or worse!'

"But why make a great fuss?
  Things are over for us.
  We must fight with the worst of our foes.

"And we've so few men here
That it's perfectly clear
Our brief tale will soon draw to its close.

"Then they'll sing on the hill,
In the glen, by the mill,
Of this terrible 15th of June,

"And that lazy young man
Who brought DOOM to his clan,
With his lute—and his charts of the Moon!"

Said the Duke, "Don't give way!
I'm convinced if today
Is the 15th of June, as you've said,

"There's no cause for alarm,
You will come to no harm.
Why, you'll wind up rejoicing instead!

"For it's now almost noon,
And I'm sure that the Moon
Will soon pass betwixt us and the Sun.

"An ECLIPSE—which will last
Till the Moon has gone past. . . .
It will start at ten minutes to one!

"So leave matters to me!"
Cried the Duke of Dundee,
"While I hatch a spectacular plan

"To deceive our great foe
With a magical show,
And to rescue the lives of our clan!"

In the meantime, MacClane
Strode about on the plain.
"Oh, I've got 'em!" He grinned like a ferret.

"In that castle I'll starve 'em,
Or in battle I'll carve 'em
Into six hundred pieces, I swear it!"

As he spoke, a small boat
Came across the wide moat,
And the oarsman alit with a bound,

A grim wizard, whose shape
Was concealed by a cape
Falling down in loose folds to the ground.

Said the Duke of Dundee,
For of course it was he,
"Sir Angus—take care—you're in danger!

"Though you may think it queer
Such a warning to hear
From the lips of an absolute stranger.

"Yes, I know your foul fame,
But I've come all the same,
To rescue a scoundrel and knave who

"Is so steeped in black crime
That there may not be time
For even a wizard to save you!

"Now-hear-this—and despair!
The Great Powers of the Air
Mean to slay you for all that you've done!

"First, to show you their might,
They'll turn day into night,
And then blot out the face of the Sun!

"So repent what you've been,
Because once they begin
From this world you will swiftly be taken,

"If you've failed to agree
To make peace with Dundee.
Heed my warning! I'm *never* mistaken!"

But Sir Angus just laughed,
And said, "Wizard, you're daft!
On that point I am certain, believe me.

"They'll turn day into night?
That *would* give me a fright,
But they can't, so don't try to deceive me!"

"Yet I think you can see,"
Said the Duke of Dundee,
"That the sunlight no longer is glowing!

"And look there! On the lawn!
  Your own shadow is gone,
  And the darkness appears to be growing!"

Then Sir Angus turned white,
  As the day changed to night,
  And his shadow?—no man could have found it.

For alas and alack,
  The bright Sun was now black,
  With mysterious flames all around it!

And MacClane to his knees
Sank at last, and said, "Please,
I'll make peace with Dundee and his clan, Sir!

"And I'll lead back my men
To our home in the glen
With all of the speed that I can, Sir!

"And I swear nevermore
To take part in a war,
Or to think up a plot, or make trouble,

"If the Powers of the Air
My poor life will just spare!
Now I'm off—and I mean on-the-double!"

Then Sir Angus MacClane
Turned his back on the plain,
And he and his terrified men,

In mad panic and fright,
Dashed away out of sight
And never were heard of again.

And the Duke of Dundee
Was received with great glee
By his gratified uncles and aunts,

Who decided to show
They'd misjudged him, and so
They arranged for a banquet and dance.

There was cake, there were speeches,
There was ice cream with peaches,
There were songs for the lute and guitar.

And they danced on the lawn
Till the pale light of dawn
Hid from sight the last twinkling star.

And that knight, ever after,
With music and laughter,
Lived a life both delightful and free,

And he always was known
In his castle of stone
As the Peace-Loving Duke of Dundee.

Printed in U.S.A.